W9-BMZ-851

Hello Kitty®
Camping Adventure

by Kris Hirschmann
Illustrated by Sachiho Hino

SCHOLASTIC INC.

ISBN 978-0-545-55036-9
© 1976, 2014 SANRIO CO., LTD.
All rights reserved. Published by Scholastic Inc., 557 Broadway, New York, NY 10012.
SCHOLASTIC and associated logos are trademarks and/or registered trademarks of Scholastic Inc.

10 9 8 7 6 5 4 3
Printed in the U.S.A.

14 15 16 17 18 19/0
40

This edition first edition printing, May 2014

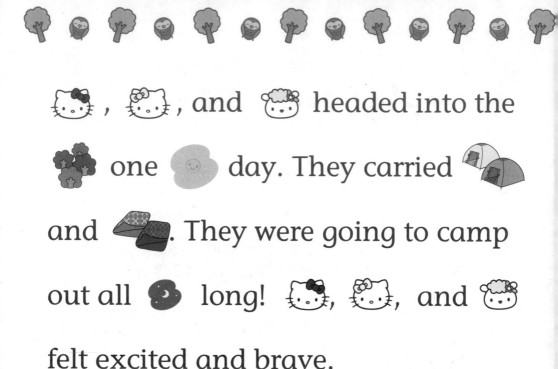

, , and headed into the one day. They carried and . They were going to camp out all long! , , and felt excited and brave.

Soon the friends found a perfect campsite. They set up their and among the .

🌙 soon fell. The friends lit a 🔥

and sat around it. They each found a

🥢 and cooked 🌭. They giggled

and sang songs.

The 🌳 were dark, but 🐱,

🐱 , and 🐑 didn't notice. They

were having too much fun.

After dinner, 🐱 , 🐱 , and 🐑

decided to tell stories around the

🔥 . 🐑 went first. She told a creepy

story about a giant 🕷 .

🐱 shivered. She suddenly noticed

the dark 🌳 . She knew she was safe

with her friends, but she felt a little

scared anyway.

At that moment, something poked

's head.  jumped up. She

told  and  that something had

touched her!

 and  jumped up, too. ,

, and  hugged one another

and peered into the . What could

it be?

Then someone familiar stepped out of the dark. It was ! was smiling and holding a . He had used the to tap !

, , and relaxed. They even laughed a little. They knew loved to play jokes on his friends.

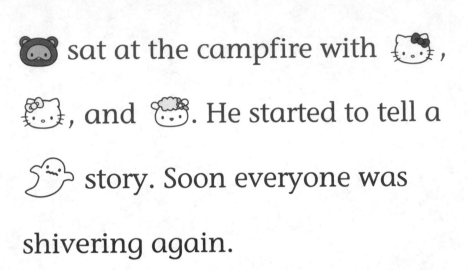 sat at the campfire with 🐱,

🐱, and 🐑. He started to tell a

👻 story. Soon everyone was

shivering again.

Just then, a spooky green

appeared in the 🌳. It looked like it

was floating! Was it a 👻?

The came closer and closer. The

friends soon saw that it wasn't a .

It was a full of ! Their friend

was carrying the .

Everyone smiled. was much

more fun than a scary !

sat down at the ⛲. He started

to tell a story about a big, mean 🌳

that lived in the 🌲.

Just then 🐱, 🐱, 🐑, 🐻, and

🐶 heard a loud rustling noise. Oh,

no! They were sure the 🌳 was

coming to get them!

But it wasn't a . It was just 🐻.

He was carrying a yummy 🍎 🥧.

🐱 had baked it especially for the

campout. What a treat! A 🥧 was a

lot better than a 👹!

realized that she had been right all along. There was nothing scary in the 🌲. Suddenly, she felt brave again.

🐱 and 🐑 felt brave, too. Still, 🐱, 🐱, and 🐑 invited 🐨, 🐶, and 🐻 to join their campout. If three friends could be brave, six could be even braver. And more friends meant more fun!

Everyone sat around the 🔥. Each

friend took a big slice of 🍎🥧.

They laughed and sang songs

instead of telling scary stories. The

six friends had the best 🌙 ever

camping in the 🌳.

Did you spot all the picture clues in this Hello Kitty book?

Each picture clue is on a flash card. Ask a grown-up to cut out the flash cards. Then try reading the words on the back of the cards. The pictures will be your clues.

Reading is fun with *Hello Kitty*!

Hello Kitty	Mimmy
Fifi	woods
sunny	tents

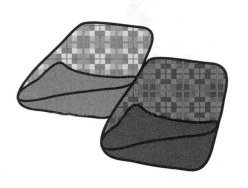

sleeping bags	night
trees	campfire
hot dogs	stick

spider	Tracy
ghost	light
jar	fireflies

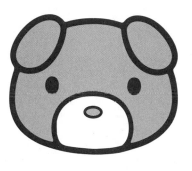

Jodie	monster
Tippy	apple
pie	Mama